Standard Grade

Maths

revision notes

Text © 2000 M. C. Davis
Design and layout © 2000 Leckie & Leckie Ltd.
Cover image © Alamy Images

12/270208

ISBN 978-1-898890-82-9

Published by
Leckie & Leckie Ltd, 3rd floor, 4 Queen Street, Edinburgh, EH2 1JE
Tel: 0131 220 6831 Fax: 0131 225 9987
enquiries@leckieandleckie.co.uk   www.leckieandleckie.co.uk

Edited by
Ken Nisbet and Isobel Vass

Special thanks to
David Collins (proofreading),
Caleb Rutherford (design) and Hamish Sanderson (illustration)

A CIP Catalogue record for this book is available from the British Library.

Leckie & Leckie Ltd is a division of Huveaux plc.

✕ M. C. Davis ✕

Contents

Introduction

What these Notes cover

These Revision Notes cover the main Knowledge and Understanding topics at General and Credit levels. The content for Credit level is indicated by  to the left of the relevant sections. If you are not sitting the Credit level exams, you may choose to ignore the Credit level content and concentrate on the content for General level. If you are sitting the General and Credit level exams then you will have to be familiar with all of the contents of these Revision Notes.

You will find the most important facts and formulae for Standard Grade Maths in the ESSENTIAL INFORMATION boxes. Many of these formulae are also printed in the actual papers to help you in the exams. Study page 56 which lists these formulae.

Another Leckie & Leckie book

To test your knowledge and understanding of Standard Grade Maths, we recommend that you obtain a copy of Leckie & Leckie's other Standard Grade Maths book, *Questions in Standard Grade Maths*, from your school, college or bookshop. It includes over 200 questions, four practice exams and a pull-out answer section

ISBN 1-898890-77-3

About the exam

> **ESSENTIAL INFORMATION**
>
> | General Exam | Paper I | 35 minutes Calculator not allowed |
> | | Paper II | 55 minutes Calculator allowed |
> | Credit Exam | Paper I | 55 minutes Calculator not allowed |
> | | Paper II | 80 minutes Calculator allowed |

What to bring to the exam

For the exam you must have a Scientific calculator (Paper II only), pens, and a pencil for diagrams. Take with you also a ruler, rubber, protractor and compasses.

Exam technique

- **Read the questions carefully.**
- **Be sure to write down all your working.** The examiners can only judge your work by what you write down, so let them see what you are thinking.
- **Check your solutions**, especially when you solve equations. Look back at the question, substitute the values you have found and make sure they work.
- **Don't panic** if the exam seems harder than you were expecting. If it really is more difficult then the pass mark will be lowered to compensate.
- **Don't just write the answer.** The examiner wants to see what Maths you can do, and that means you must **show your working**. If there is a question you find difficult, try substituting easy numbers and then see if you can do it. Then use the same method with the difficult numbers.

Your calculator

Make sure you have your own Scientific calculator and that you know how to operate it. Borrowing someone else's for the exam is not the same, since each type of calculator has slight differences from the others.

> **TIP**
>
> Check that the answers you get with your calculator are sensible!

Using your calculator properly

Learn to use your own calculator properly. Using it properly cuts down the routine calculation work – and the time it takes. For example, to enter the number 3.2×10^{-5} on most calculators, the key sequence is 3·2 $\boxed{\text{Exp}}$ 5 $\boxed{+/-}$. Is yours like this? How does the number appear on **your** calculator's display? Calculators vary – you need to be familiar with yours.

Scientific calculators will give an answer in scientific notation if you enter a calculation which has a very large or very small answer. Other calculators will give an error message instead. Check your own calculator if you are not sure by doing something like 8 000 000 × 3 000 000.

Good Credit level students who can operate their calculators well will be able to evaluate formulae directly on their calculators without doing any rounding in the middle. In this book, some extra working lines have been included to help students who are not quite so confident. Bypass these lines if you can get the answers directly using your calculator.

Calculators sometimes give **approximate** values, e.g. for cos 45° or for $\sqrt{40}$. When your calculator only gives an approximate value, do not use it if the question asks for an **exact** value. Here are two examples to show when you should and should not use your calculator:

- **Example 1: when to use your calculator**
  A square has an area of 20 cm². What is the length of its sides?
  Length = $\sqrt{20}$ = 4·47 cm. (No problem about using your calculator here.)

- **Example 2: when not to use your calculator**
  Express $\sqrt{20}$ as a surd in its simplest form.
  4·47 is not a surd – it is only an approximation for $\sqrt{20}$, so you cannot use a calculator here.
  $20 = 2^2 \times 5$, so $\sqrt{20} = 2\sqrt{5}$.

> **TIP**
>
> Use your common sense and write down your working!

> **TIP**
>
> Don't turn to your calculator every time you have to do negative numbers or fractions – you will lose your important non-calculator skills if you don't practise them!

1. Testing your Calculation Skills

This chapter contains practice questions to test your calculation skills.

> **ESSENTIAL INFORMATION**
>
> 'Calculate' does **not** mean 'use a calculator'!
> 'Calculate' means 'work out'. Sometimes you can use a calculator to help, but in Paper I all the calculating is to be done by your brain.
> Do not use a calculator for anything in this chapter.

How to work through these questions

When you are working through these practice questions, first cover up the 'Working out and tips' and 'Answers' and look only at the question.
Work through all the questions, doing everything you can.
Then look at the answers given and check your own answers.
Finally, use the 'Working out and tips' to help you with those you could not do. (You may, however, have a different method of working out the answer from the method given.)

> **ESSENTIAL INFORMATION**
>
> Remember to attempt each question yourself before looking at the tips and answers.

General level questions

Remember – no calculator!

Question	Working out and tips	Answer
• Calculate: 30% of £76	10% is £7·60, then × 3	£22·80
1·08 × 60	1·08 × 10 = 10·8, then × 6	64·8
$3 \times 7\frac{1}{2}$	$3 \times 7 = 21$ $3 \times \frac{1}{2} = 1\frac{1}{2}$	$22\frac{1}{2}$
17·9 − 2·3 + 4·1	Remember, the sign **before** the number tells you what to do with it.	19·7
17 − 9·4	17·0 −9·4	7·6
41·9 ÷ 5	remainders absolutely not allowed 5)41·90	8·38
47 × 13	long multiplication: since 13 is 10 + 3, do 47 × 10 and 47 × 3, then add the answers	611
8175·3 ÷ 300	÷ 100 to get 81·753, then divide by 3	27·251

Remember – no calculator!

Question	Working out and tips	Answer
• **Simplify:** $3(x - 2y)$	Multiply each term in the bracket by 3.	$3x - 6y$
$6a - 5a + 2a$	This is rather like $6 - 5 + 2$, since all terms contain 'a'.	$3a$
$(3x)^2$	means $3x \times 3x$	$9x^2$
$2a + 3b + 5a$	Collect 'a' terms and 'b' terms separately.	$7a + 3b$
$\left(\dfrac{1}{4}\right)^3$	$\dfrac{1}{4} \times \dfrac{1}{4} \times \dfrac{1}{4}$	$\dfrac{1}{64}$
2^5	means $2 \times 2 \times 2 \times 2 \times 2$ (Don't add!)	32
$\sqrt{81}$	$81 = 9 \times 9$	9
• **Express:** 17 381 to the nearest hundred	The '81' has to go! However, 81 is more than half of a hundred, so round up.	17 400
3·8246 to two decimal places	The '46' has to go! However, since 4 is less than 5, don't round up.	3·82
17·3 km in metres	$17·3 \times 1000$	17 300 metres
• **Calculate:** $-2 + 6$	think of a number line: start at -2, go up 6	4
$3 + (-5)$	adding a negative means go **down** number line	-2
$1\frac{3}{4} + 2\frac{1}{2}$	add whole numbers: 3 fractions: change to quarters $\frac{3}{4} + \frac{1}{2} = \frac{3}{4} + \frac{2}{4} = \frac{5}{4} = 1\frac{1}{4}$	$4\frac{1}{4}$
$\frac{4}{5}$ of 30 m	Find $\frac{1}{5}$ (divide by 5): 6 m $\frac{4}{5}$ is 4 times as much: 24 m	24 m
• **Factorise:** $2x + 4y$	2 is the common factor so put it outside the brackets	$2(x + 2y)$

Credit level questions

Remember – no calculator!

Question	Working out and tips	Answer
• **Calculate:** $-5 - (-9)$	subtracting a negative is equivalent to adding: $-5 + 9$	4
$\dfrac{-24}{-6}$	for the signs, remember: +ve × −ve = −ve −ve × −ve = +ve (same for division) now do the division $\frac{24}{6}$	4
$16 - 7{\cdot}5 \div 5$	$16 - 1{\cdot}5$ × and ÷ take priority over + and −	14·5
$\frac{3}{5}$ of $6\frac{1}{4}$	$\frac{3}{5} \times \frac{25}{4}$	$\frac{15}{4}$
$\left(\frac{1}{6} + \frac{1}{4}\right) \div \frac{1}{3}$	$\frac{2}{12} + \frac{3}{12} = \frac{5}{12}$ $\div \frac{1}{3}$ is same as $\times 3$	$\frac{5}{4}$
$2\frac{1}{2} \div \frac{1}{3}$	$\dfrac{2\frac{1}{2} \times 3}{\frac{1}{3} \times 3} = \dfrac{7\frac{1}{2}}{1} = 7\frac{1}{2}$ (You may have a different method.)	$7\frac{1}{2}$ or 7·5
• **Round to three significant figures:** 60 082 0·00041635	The first non-zero digit from the left is the first significant figure. Take it and the next two figures. Decide whether you need to round up by looking at the next again figure. Fill in with zeros as required.	60 100 0·000416
• **Simplify:** $a^3 \times a^5$	to multiply powers of a, add indices	a^8
$\dfrac{a^6}{a^2}$	to divide powers of a, subtract indices	a^4
• **Express:** £3·7 million in full	$3{\cdot}7 \times 1\,000\,000$	£3 700 000
24·5 million in Scientific notation	$24{\cdot}5 \times 1\,000\,000$ 24 500 000	$2{\cdot}45 \times 10^7$

Remember – no calculator!

Question	Working out and tips	Answer
• **Simplify:**		
$\sqrt{20}$	$\sqrt{2\times2\times5}$ (split into prime factors)	$2\sqrt{5}$
$(27)^{\frac{1}{3}}$	$(3\times3\times3)^{\frac{1}{3}}$ (power $\frac{1}{3}$ means cube root)	3
$3\sqrt{54}$	$3\times\sqrt{2\times3\times3\times3}=3\times3\times\sqrt{2\times3}$	$9\sqrt{6}$
$\left(\dfrac{9}{16}\right)^{\frac{1}{2}}$	$=\dfrac{9^{\frac{1}{2}}}{16^{\frac{1}{2}}}$ (power $\frac{1}{2}$ means square root)	$\dfrac{3}{4}$
$5\sqrt{2}-2\sqrt{2}$	compare with $5a-2a$	$3\sqrt{2}$
$\dfrac{10a^2-3ab-b^2}{15a+3b}$	factorise: $\dfrac{(5a+b)(2a-b)}{3(5a+b)}$	$\dfrac{2a-b}{3}$
$\dfrac{5-2x}{3}-\dfrac{8x-3}{2x+1}$	$\dfrac{(5-2x)(2x+1)}{3(2x+1)}-\dfrac{3(8x-3)}{3(2x+1)}$ $=\dfrac{10x+5-4x^2-2x-24x+9}{3(2x+1)}$	$\dfrac{14-16x-4x^2}{3(2x+1)}$
$(a^2)^3$	$a^{2\times3}$ To raise to a power, multiply indices	a^6
$\dfrac{1}{p^{-2}}$	$p^{-2}=\dfrac{1}{p^2}$ so $\dfrac{1}{p^{-2}}=p^2$	p^2
$\dfrac{y^5}{y^{-2}}$	subtract indices: $y^{5-(-2)}$	y^7
$3a^{-\frac{1}{2}}\left(a^{\frac{1}{2}}+a^{-\frac{3}{2}}\right)$	$3a^{-\frac{1}{2}}\times a^{\frac{1}{2}}=3a^{-\frac{1}{2}+\frac{1}{2}}$ and $a^0=1$ $3a^{-\frac{1}{2}}\times a^{-\frac{3}{2}}=3a^{-\frac{1}{2}+\left(-\frac{3}{2}\right)}$	$3+3a^{-2}$
• **Express with rational denominator:**		
$\dfrac{3}{\sqrt{20}}$	$\dfrac{3}{\sqrt{4\times5}}=\dfrac{3}{2\sqrt{5}}\times\dfrac{\sqrt{5}}{\sqrt{5}}=\dfrac{3\sqrt{5}}{2\times5}$	$\dfrac{3\sqrt{5}}{10}$

2. Formulae and Equations

Making and using formulae

- **Example 1**

  Look at these patterns of black tiles and white tiles:

   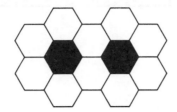 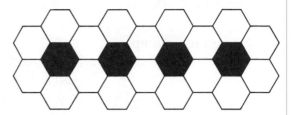

  What is the formula linking the number of black tiles and the number of white tiles?

  Make a table:

black b	1	2	3	4	5	etc
white w	6	10	14	18	22	etc

  Notice that the value of w goes up by 4 each time, so the formula will have '$4b$' in it. Work out the values for $4b$:

$4b$	4	8	12	16	20	etc

  Now it's clear that w is always 2 more than $4b$.

  Formula: $w = 4b + 2$

  > **TIP**
  >
  > Always **check your formula** for other values in your table.
  > If it doesn't **always** work, either the formula or the table is wrong!

- **Example 2**

  Here is an example of **substitution** into a formula:
  The formula for the height of a stone t seconds after it is thrown vertically upwards is:

  $$h = ut - 5t^2$$

  where h is the height of the stone in metres,
  u is the speed in metres per second at which the stone is thrown and
  t is the time in seconds.

  A stone is thrown vertically upwards at a speed of 30 m/s. What is its height after 2 seconds?

  Substituting $t = 2$ and $u = 30$ into the formula gives:

  $$h = 30 \times 2 - 5 \times 2^2$$
  $$= 60 - 20$$
  $$= 40$$

  The height is 40 metres.

Equations and inequalities

- **Equation example**
  $3x + 9 = x + 5$ Find x.
  $$3x + 9 = x + 5$$
  Take x from both sides: $2x + 9 = 5$
  Take 9 from both sides: $2x = -4$
  Divide both sides by 2: $x = -2$

- **Inequality example**
  Solve $3n > 7$, where n is a whole number.
  $$3n > 7$$
  Divide both sides by 3: $n > \frac{7}{3}$, so $n > 2\frac{1}{3}$
  So, since n is a whole number, $n = 3, 4, 5$, etc.

More equations and inequalities

- **Another equation example**

  Jane's backpack weighed twice as much as Anne's, but by transferring 1 kg of Jane's load to Anne's pack, Anne had two-thirds as much weight as Jane. What weight was each girl carrying at the start?

  Let x stand for Anne's load at the start, so Jane's is $2x$.
  After the transfer: Anne has $x + 1$
                         Jane has $2x - 1$

  so: $x + 1 = \frac{2}{3}(2x - 1)$
  multiply both sides by 3 to remove fractions: $3x + 3 = 2(2x - 1)$
  which gives: $x = 5$ (check for yourself)
  So to begin with, Anne's pack weighed 5 kg and Jane's 10 kg.

- **Another inequality example**

  Solve the inequality: $\dfrac{2x + 1}{4} - \dfrac{2x - 1}{3} \leqslant \dfrac{5}{6}$

  Multiply both sides by 12: $3(2x + 1) - 4(2x - 1) \leqslant 10$
                                $6x + 3 - 8x + 4 \leqslant 10$
                                      $-2x \leqslant 3$
                                      $2x \geqslant -3$
                                      $x \geqslant -1{\cdot}5$

ESSENTIAL INFORMATION

If you multiply or divide an inequality by something negative, you must change round the inequality sign.

Proving/disproving a conjecture

- Look again at the formula on page 9 for the design of black tiles and white tiles.
  You can **check** that $w = 4b + 2$ for particular values of b.
  Can you **prove** that $w = 4b + 2$ for **all** values of b?
  Here is one of the patterns divided up into several sections:

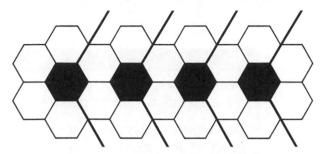

  And then pulled apart:

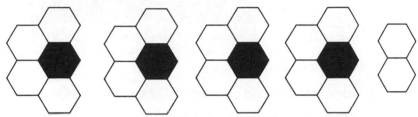

  Each section has one black tile and four white tiles. Two extra white tiles are also needed at the end. You can see that however many sections the pattern has, this will always be true.
  So the number of white tiles will always be four times the number of black tiles, plus two.
  That is, $w = 4b + 2$.

- If a conjecture is **not true**, it can be disproved by finding just one counter example.
  Conjecture: If n is an integer, n^2 is odd.
  You can take $n = 2$ to give a counter example.
  If $n = 2$, then $n^2 = 4$, and n^2 is not odd.
  Since you have found a counter example, you have shown that the conjecture is false.

Factorisation and brackets

If there are brackets, 'simplify' will involve multiplying out to remove them. 'Factorise' in algebra usually means putting brackets in. Here are some examples and tips:

Question	Working out and tips	Answer
• **Simplify:** $3x(y + 2x)$	Multiply each term in the brackets by $3x$	$3xy + 6x^2$
• **Factorise:** $a^2 - b^2$	difference of 2 squares	$(a - b)(a + b)$
$3x^2 + 5x$	x is common to both terms. Put this common factor outside the brackets.	$x(3x + 5)$
$x^2 - 3x - 10$	This is a quadratic expression. Factorise first and last terms, then check middle term.	$(x - 5)(x + 2)$
• **Factorise:** $4a^2 - 25b^2$	$(2a)^2 - (5b)^2$ difference of 2 squares	$(2a - 5b)(2a + 5b)$

More about formulae

- **Example 1**

  The formula for the volume of a cone is: $V = \frac{1}{3}\pi r^2 h$

  Change the subject of this formula to r, and then find the radius of a cone which has a height of 10 cm and holds 1 litre.

  Multiply both sides by 3: $3V = \pi r^2 h$
  Change sides over: $\pi r^2 h = 3V$

  Divide both sides by πh: $r^2 = \dfrac{3V}{\pi h}$

  $$r = \pm\sqrt{\dfrac{3V}{\pi h}}$$

  > **TIP**
  >
  > Here, you only consider the +ve root, since the radius must be positive.
  >
  > Don't forget to say **why** you are rejecting one possible answer.

  Substitute values: $r = +\sqrt{\dfrac{3 \times 1000}{\pi \times 10}}$

  > **TIP**
  >
  > Remember to change litres into cm³.

  $= 9{\cdot}8$ (to one decimal place)

  so radius is 9·8 cm (to one decimal place)

- **Example 2**

  What would the effect be on the volume of a cone if the radius of the base were increased by 20%, but the height remained unchanged?

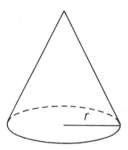

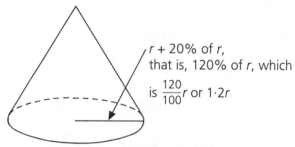

r + 20% of r, that is, 120% of r, which is $\frac{120}{100}r$ or $1{\cdot}2r$

  Volume of cone before the increase:

  $$V_1 = \tfrac{1}{3}\pi r^2 h$$

  Volume of cone after the increase:

  $$V_2 = \tfrac{1}{3}\pi (1{\cdot}2r)^2 h$$
  $$= 1{\cdot}44 \times \tfrac{1}{3}\pi r^2 h$$
  $$= 1{\cdot}44 \times V_1$$

  So the volume would be multiplied by a factor of 1·44.

- **Example 3**

  Evaluate $v^2 - 2uv$ where $u = 5$ and $v = -3$

  $= (-3)^2 - (2 \times 5 \times (-3))$

  $= 9 - (-30)$

  $= 39$

  > **TIP**
  >
  > Expect questions like example 3 to appear in Paper I, where you cannot use a calculator!

Quadratic equations

> **TIP**
>
> Expect to find **two** solutions to any quadratic equation, although the solutions might be the same.

- **Example 1**
  Solve: $x^2 - 9x = 0$
  Take out the common factor: $x(x - 9) = 0$
  So $x = 0$ or $x = 9$

- **Example 2**

9 cm

4 cm

When all the sides of this rectangle are increased by the same amount, the area is 73 cm².

Find this increase, correct to one decimal place.

Let x be the increase, so for the new rectangle: length $= 9 + x$
breadth $= 4 + x$

So area of rectangle $= (9 + x)(4 + x) = 73$
$$36 + 13x + x^2 = 73$$
$$x^2 + 13x - 37 = 0$$

This is the **standard quadratic form**. Always arrange terms in this order.

> **TIP**
>
> If a quadratic equation will factorise, factorising it will be the quickest way to solve it. This equation doesn't factorise, however, so you must use the quadratic formula.

> **ESSENTIAL INFORMATION**
>
> The quadratic formula gives the solutions of $ax^2 + bx + c = 0$
>
> $$x = \frac{-b \pm \sqrt{b^2 - 4ac}}{2a}$$

For the equation above, $a = 1$, $b = 13$, $c = -37$

Substituting: $x = \dfrac{-13 \pm \sqrt{169 + 148}}{2}$

$$= \frac{-13 \pm \sqrt{317}}{2}$$

$$= 2 \cdot 4 \text{ or } -15 \cdot 4$$

A negative answer would not make sense for an increase – look back at the diagram.

> **TIP**
>
> If you reject one of the solutions, always remember to say why.

So the increase is 2·4 cm, to one decimal place.

3. Shape

Measurement

The metric system is based on the metre (length), litre (volume) and gram (mass or weight).

ESSENTIAL INFORMATION

Length	Volume	Mass
10 mm = 1 cm	1000 ml = 1 litre	1000 g = 1 kg
100 cm = 1 m	1000 cm³ = 1 litre	1000 kg = 1 tonne
1000 m = 1 km		

Angles

- **Right angle, 90°**

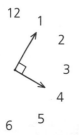

- **Straight angle or a half turn, 180°**

- **One revolution or a whole turn, 360°**

In the next three diagrams, equal angles have been labelled with the same letter.

- **Vertically opposite angles**

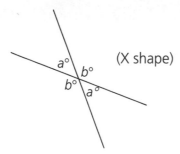

(X shape)

- **Alternate angles**

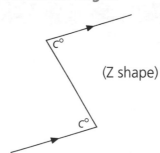

(Z shape)

- **Corresponding angles**

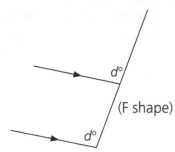

(F shape)

For angles to be alternate or corresponding, the lines marked ➤ must be parallel.

- **Angle sum in a triangle**

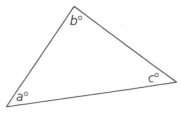

$a° + b° + c° = 180°$
for every triangle

- **Angle sum in a polygon**
  Divide the polygon into triangles, then count multiples of 180°.

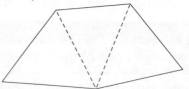

There are three triangles in this pentagon (5-sided polygon), so there are $3 × 180°$ giving a total of 540° for the angle sum.

Symmetry

- **Bilateral symmetry**

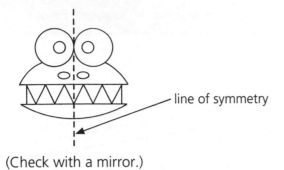

line of symmetry

(Check with a mirror.)

- **Rotational symmetry**

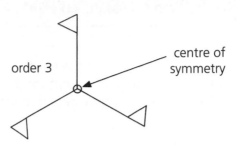

order 3

centre of symmetry

(Check with tracing paper –
pivot the paper round the centre.)

Two-dimensional shapes

- If you know what lines of symmetry a shape has, and whether it has rotational symmetry, you can work out the properties of its sides, angles and diagonals.

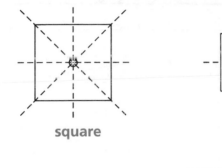

square

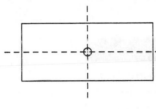

rectangle

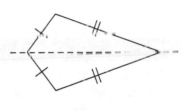

kite

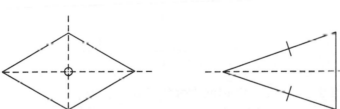

rhombus

isosceles triangle

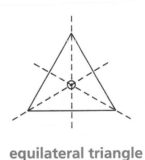

equilateral triangle

- A **parallelogram** has no lines of symmetry but does have half-turn symmetry:

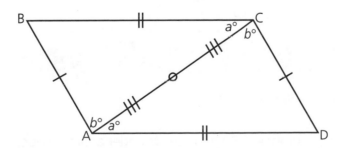

Triangle ABC is congruent to (fits exactly on top of) triangle CDA, so you can pick out equal sides and angles.

Area of two-dimensional shapes

ESSENTIAL INFORMATION

Area of rectangle = length × breadth	Area of triangle = $\frac{1}{2}$ × base × height

- **Example**
  This picture shows the front view of a greenhouse. It is all glass except for the door. Find the area of glass required for the front.

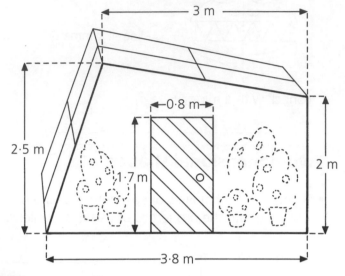

TIP

All straight-edged shapes can be divided up into triangles and rectangles, so you can find the area of any straight-edged shape.

Draw a plan and divide it up.

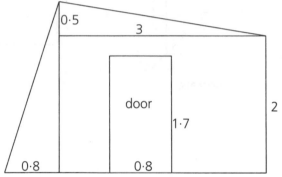

Find the total area of the front:
area of top triangle: $\frac{1}{2} \times 0.5 \times 3 = 0.75$
area of side triangle: $\frac{1}{2} \times 0.8 \times 2.5 = 1$
area of large rectangle: $3 \times 2 = 6$
               total area: 7·75 m²
Take away area of door: $1.7 \times 0.8 = 1.36$ m²
so   area of glass = 6·39 m²

Tolerance

Measurements are never completely accurate.

- **Example**
  If you examined a large number of 30 mm screws under a microscope, you would find some a bit longer than 30 mm, and some a bit shorter.

  If the manufacturer claimed they all measured 30 mm ± 0·2 mm, what would be their greatest and least possible lengths?
  30 mm + 0·2 mm = 30·2 mm is the greatest length they could be.
  30 mm − 0·2 mm = 29·8 mm is the least length they could be.

Three-dimensional shapes

cone

cylinder

cuboid

triangular prism

sphere

- When a model of a solid is made from straws and pipecleaners, it is easy to see its **edges** (the straws), and its **vertices** or corners (where the pipecleaners go).

A square-based pyramid has 5 vertices and 8 edges.

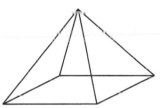

- When a model is constructed from a net drawn on card, its **faces** are easily seen:

A net of a cuboid has 6 faces, all rectangular.

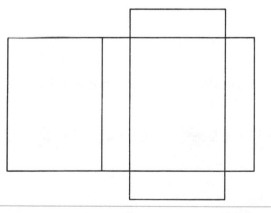

Surface area and volume

- **Surface area example**
  What area of canvas is needed to make this tent, which has a canvas floor section too?

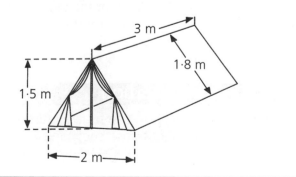

3 m

1·8 m

1·5 m

2 m

Surface area and volume (cont.)

TIP

Drawing a net helps here.
Write in the dimensions on the net.

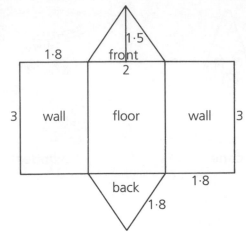

area of floor $= 3 \times 2$ $= 6 \cdot 0 \text{ m}^2$

area of left wall $= 3 \times 1 \cdot 8$ $= 5 \cdot 4 \text{ m}^2$

area of right wall $= 3 \times 1 \cdot 8$ $= 5 \cdot 4 \text{ m}^2$

area of front $= \frac{1}{2} \times 2 \times 1 \cdot 5 = 1 \cdot 5 \text{ m}^2$

area of back $= \frac{1}{2} \times 2 \times 1 \cdot 5 = 1 \cdot 5 \text{ m}^2$

total area $= 19 \cdot 8 \text{ m}^2$

- **Volume of prisms**
  - Prisms have the same **cross-section** all the way up. There are two triangular prisms on page 17: the place card and the tent. (The shape of their cross-sections is triangular.) Here are some other prisms (and, in brackets, the shape of their cross-sections):

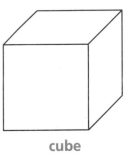
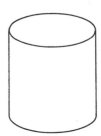
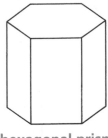
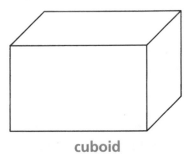

cube	cylinder	hexagonal prism	cuboid
(square)	(circle)	(hexagon)	(rectangle)

ESSENTIAL INFORMATION

	Volume of prism = cross-sectional area × length
or	Volume of prism = area of base × height
or	V = Ah

- **Example**
  Let's now find the volume of the tent shown on page 17. (Remember it is a triangular prism.)
  cross-sectional area $= 1 \cdot 5 \text{ m}^2$ (this is the front or back)
           length $= 3 \text{ m}$
       So volume $= 1 \cdot 5 \times 3 = 4 \cdot 5 \text{ m}^3$

ESSENTIAL INFORMATION

area   – remember to use square units!
volume – remember to use cubic units!

More on surface area and volume

- **Example**
  This tank is a cylinder with hemispherical ends. Its diameter is 3 metres and it holds 57 500 litres.

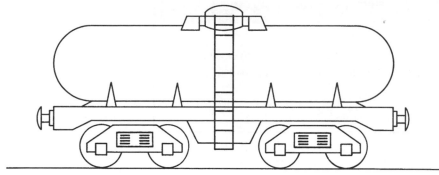

Volume of sphere = $\frac{4}{3}\pi r^3$ Surface area of sphere = $4\pi r^2$

- What is its total length?
  The two curved end sections together make a sphere of radius 1·5 m.
  Volume of hemispherical ends = $\frac{4}{3} \times \pi \times 1\cdot5^3$ = 14·14 m³
  but total volume = 57 500 litres = 57·5 m³ (since 1 m³ = 1000 litres)
  so volume of cylindrical section = 57·5 − 14·14 = 43·36 m³

  but volume of cylinder = $\pi r^2 h$ = $\pi \times 1\cdot5^2 \times h$
  so $\pi \times 1\cdot5^2 \times h$ = 43·36

  and $h = \dfrac{43\cdot36}{\pi \times 1\cdot5^2}$ = 6·1 m.

TIP

Remember that 43·36 is to be divided by π and divided by 1·5², that is 43·36 ÷ ($\pi \times 1\cdot5^2$).

The key sequence 43·36 ÷ 3·14 × 1·5² will give you the wrong answer.

Make sure now that you can find a **correct key sequence**.

Total length of tank is 6·1 + (2 × 1·5) = 9·1 metres

- Find the surface area of the tank.
  The surface area is made up of two parts: the surface of a sphere and the curved surface of a cylinder, which when unrolled gives a rectangle.
  Sphere: area = $4\pi r^2$ = $4 \times \pi \times 1\cdot5^2$ = 28·3 m²
  Cylinder: length is 6·1 m, breadth is $2\pi r$ which is $2 \times \pi \times 1\cdot5$
              area = $6\cdot1 \times 2 \times \pi \times 1\cdot5$ = 57·5 m²

  Total surface area = 28·3 + 57·5 = 86 m² (This is correct to the nearest m².)

4. Arithmetic

Scientific notation (Standard form)

> **ESSENTIAL INFORMATION**
>
> $a \times 10^n$ a must be between 1 and 10.
>
> n is positive for numbers greater than 10
>   and is negative for numbers less than 1.
>
> $10^1 = 10$
> $10^0 = 1$

Large numbers: 139 000 000 000 is written as $1 \cdot 39 \times 10^{11}$
                 3×10^6 is the number 3 000 000.

Small numbers: $0 \cdot 00000026$ is written as $2 \cdot 6 \times 10^{-7}$
                 $3 \cdot 576 \times 10^{-1}$ is the number $0 \cdot 3576$

Make sure you know how to enter and use these on your calculator – see page 4.

Percentage discount

- **Example**
  What is the reduction on this can of soup, expressed as a percentage of the original price?

  Reduction = 49p – 41p = 8p

  Percentage discount $= \dfrac{8}{49} \times 100$

  $= 16 \cdot 3\%$

Insurance premiums

- **Example 1**
  Use the table below to find the cost of holiday insurance for two people going on a fortnight's package holiday to Spain.

Period	Holiday insurance (cost per person)		
	Europe	USA	Outwith Europe and USA
up to 9 days	£18·90	£35·60	£38·40
10 to 17 days	£22·90	£59·80	£68·40
18 to 31 days	£32·90	£79·80	£85·00

A fortnight is two weeks, that is 14 days, so you look in the row for 'up to 17 days' and, as Spain is in Europe, you look at the Europe column.

The premium is £22·90 per person, so two people will pay a total of £45·80.

Insurance premiums (cont.)

- **Example 2**

The contents of Lorna's flat are worth £12 000. She wants to insure them with a company whose premium is £0·75 per £100 insured. She is entitled to a 7·5% discount because she has a burglar alarm and high quality locks on her door.

Find her annual premium.

£12 000 is 120 × £100, so basic premium is £0·75 × 120 = £90
Discount = 7·5% of £90 = £6·75. Subtract this from £90.
Her annual premium is £83·25.

Time, distance and speed

- **Example 1**
  Khalid wants to find the total time for his three trials in the 1500 m event. His times are 4:53, 5:08 and 4:48. (4:53 means 4 minutes and 53 seconds.)

  Seconds: 53 + 8 + 48 gives 109 seconds. 109 seconds is 1 minute and 49 seconds.

  Minutes: 4 + 5 + 4 = 13

  The total time is 13 minutes + 1 minute 49 seconds, which is:
  14 minutes 49 seconds.

- **Example 2**

  - Lesley left Inverness at 0945 and arrived in Edinburgh at 1420. How long did she spend travelling?

    0945 to 1000 is 15 minutes
    1000 to 1400 is 4 hours
    1400 to 1420 is 20 minutes

    Altogether this is 4 hours 35 minutes.

- The distance from Inverness to Edinburgh is 158 miles. Work out the average speed for Lesley's journey in miles per hour, to one decimal place.

ESSENTIAL INFORMATION

$$T = \frac{D}{S} \qquad S = \frac{D}{T} \qquad D = ST$$

Here you will use $S = \dfrac{D}{T}$

D = 158 miles

T = 4 hours 35 minutes
$= 4\frac{35}{60} = 4·583$ hours (since 35 ÷ 60 = 0·583)

$$S = \frac{D}{T} = \frac{158 \text{ miles}}{4·583 \text{ hours}} = 34·47 \text{ mph}$$

Lesley's average speed was 34·5 miles per hour, to one decimal place.

Simple interest

- **Example**
  Neil deposits £300 in a Building Society account which pays 6% interest per annum.
  What interest will he gain after 2 months?
  Interest for 1 year = 6% of £300 = £18   Interest for 2 months = $\frac{2}{12}$ of £18 = £3

Earnings

Gross pay is total earnings, i.e. basic pay plus overtime, commission, bonuses etc.
Net pay ('take home pay') is gross pay minus deductions (income tax, national insurance, superannuation, etc).

- **Example 1**
  James's basic hourly rate is £6·14. One evening he does 3 hours overtime at time and a half.
  What does he earn for this overtime?

  He will earn $1\frac{1}{2}$ times as much as usual. So his overtime rate is £6·14 × 1·5 = £9·21 per hour.

  Overtime pay = £9·21 × 3 = £27·63

- **Example 2**
  Janice earns 14% commission on all her sales. Her sales total is £2400. What is her commission?

  £2400 × 0·14 = £336

Percentage calculations

- **Example 1**
  A garage bill, including VAT at 17·5%, totals £216·32. What is the amount of the bill before VAT is added?

  If you let x represent the amount before VAT, £x + VAT = £216·32
  In percentages, 100% + 17·5% = 117·5% so 117·5% of £x is £216·32 and you need to find 100% of £x.

  117·5% $\longleftrightarrow$ £216·32

  1% $\longleftrightarrow$ £$\frac{216·32}{117·5}$

  100% $\longleftrightarrow$ £$\frac{216·32}{117·5}$ × 100 = £184·10 (to the nearest penny)

- **Example 2**
  In a sale, the price of a jacket is reduced by 12% and it now costs £49·99. What was the original price?

  In percentages, 100% − 12% = 88%

  so work out £49·99 × $\frac{100}{88}$, which gives £56·81. (You can work this out in full as in example 1.)

Compound interest and depreciation

> **TIP**
>
> Compound interest and depreciation are worked out in the same way (and so is paying back a bank loan).
>
> Work out the interest or depreciation separately each time – it will not stay the same.

- **Example 1**

Fiona buys a second-hand car for £4300. It depreciates at a rate of 20% each year.

What will it be worth after she has had it for 2 years?

Value at start = £4300
1st year's depreciation   = 20% of £4300 = £860
Value at end of 1st year = £(4300 – 860) = £3440
2nd year's depreciation   = 20% of £3440 = £688
Value at end of 2nd year = £(3440 – 688) = £2752
After 2 years Fiona's car will be worth £2752.

> **TIP**
>
> Another way to work this out is shown below. This way is useful if you are doing examples with letters instead of figures, as in example 2 below.

Value at start   = £4300

It loses 20% of its value each year and so at the end of the year is only worth 80% of its value at the start of that year.

Value at end of 1st year = 80% of £4300 = $0.8 \times £4300$
Value at end of 2nd year = 80% of value at end of 1st year
$$= 0.8 \times (0.8 \times £4300) = (0.8)^2 \times £4300 = £2752$$

- **Example 2**
Fiona buys a car for £A, and it depreciates at a rate of 30% per annum. Show that it will be worth $£(0.7)^2A$ after 2 years, and write down an expression for its value after 4 years.
Value at start   = £A
Value after 1 year   = 70% of £A = $£(0.7)A$
Value after 2 years = 70% of $£(0.7)A = 0.7 \times 0.7A = £(0.7)^2A$

> **TIP**
>
> Can you spot the pattern? A, $(0.7)A$, $(0.7)^2A$ ... $(0.7)^nA$ ...

An expression for the value of the car after 4 years is $£(0.7)^4A$.

5. Graphs and Functions

Graphs as pictures

- **Example 1**
  If you have ever filled a bottle from a tap, you'll know how the water level rises slowly for a while then suddenly rises quickly when it gets to the narrow neck.

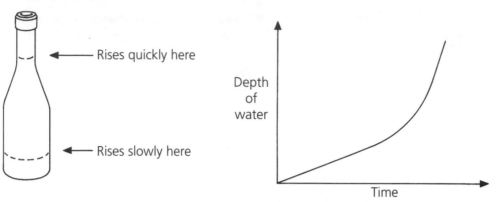

- **Example 2**
  Here is a drawing of a rollercoaster. Below it a graph has been drawn to show how the speed varies as the car goes from the start to the halfway point.

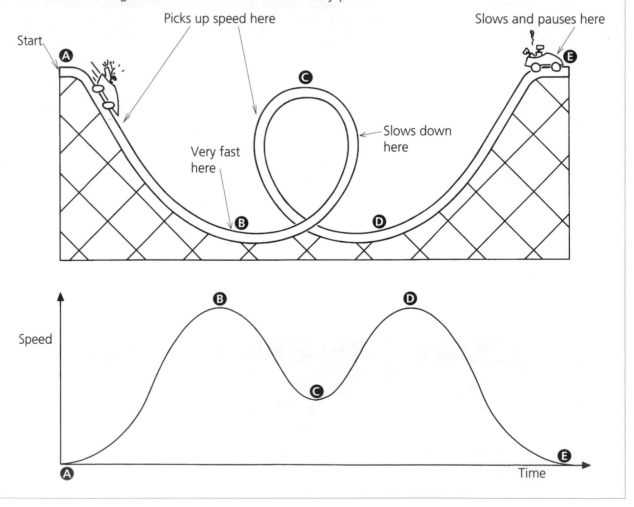

© Leckie & Leckie

Straight line graphs

- **Example**

Fit'n'Firm Health Club charges £5 a visit, but no membership fee. BodyGlow Health Club charges a membership fee of £20, plus £2 a visit. Show on a graph the cost of each club for different numbers of visits. What advice would you give to a friend who wants to join the cheaper club?

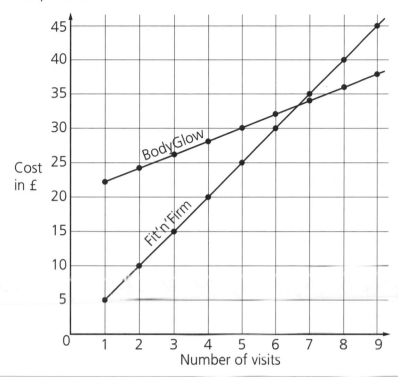

TIP

The points have been plotted and lines drawn to show the trends.

Notice that the two lines cross between 6 and 7 visits.

For up to 6 visits Fit'n'Firm is cheaper, but for **7** or more BodyGlow is cheaper.

Linear functions and graphs

ESSENTIAL INFORMATION

$y = mx + c$ This is the equation of a straight line with gradient m which cuts the y-axis at $(0, c)$.

An equation may need to be rearranged before you can tell its gradient and y-intercept.

- **Example**

What is the gradient of the line $3x + 2y = 8$? Where does it cut the y-axis?

$3x + 2y = 8$
$2y = -3x + 8$
$y = -\frac{3}{2}x + 4$

Compare with $y = mx + c$
so gradient is $-\frac{3}{2}$,
The line cuts the y-axis at $(0, 4)$.

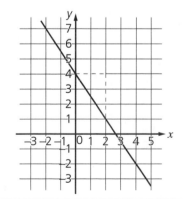

TIP

Gradient $-\frac{3}{2}$ means the line comes **down 3** units for every **2 along**.

Quadratic functions

> **ESSENTIAL INFORMATION**
>
> $f(x) = ax^2 + bx + c$, where a, b and c are constants, is the equation of a quadratic function. Its graph is a parabola.

- **Example**

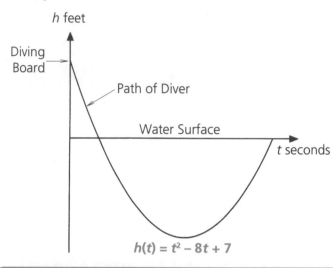

This graph $h(t) = t^2 - 8t + 7$ shows the position of a diver's head during a dive, plotted against the time since she left the diving board.

When did she resurface?
How long was she under water?
What was the lowest depth she reached?

> **TIP**
>
> When she hit the water and when she resurfaced, $h(t) = 0$.

so $t^2 - 8t + 7 = 0$
$(t - 1)(t - 7) = 0$ (by factorising the quadratic)
so $t = 1$ or $t = 7$

This means the diver hit the water after 1 second, and resurfaced after 7 seconds. She was underwater for 6 seconds.

> **TIP**
>
> The graph is symmetrical (the axis of symmetry is $t = 4$), so she reached the lowest depth halfway between 1 second and 7 seconds, that is after 4 seconds. So find h when $t = 4$.

$h(4) = 4^2 - 8 \times 4 + 7 = 16 - 32 + 7 = -9$ (4, –9) is the minimum turning point for the above graph.

So she dived to a depth of 9 feet.

Simultaneous equations

- **Example: two linear equations**
  Find the point of intersection of these two lines: $3x - 2y = 8$ .... (1)
                                                            $5x + 8y = 70$ .... (2)

To eliminate y, you multiply equation (1) by 4: $12x - 8y = 32$
                                      equation (2): $5x + 8y = 70$
                                                         ————————————
Now add: $17x = 102$
Solve for x: $x = 6$
Substitute this value into equation (1): $3 \times 6 - 2y = 8$
Solve for y: $-2y = -10$
                                                             $y = 5$

The point of intersection is (6, 5).

Graph of $f(x) = a^x$ (exponential function)

- **Example**
A smart 12-year-old made a deal with her parents regarding pocket money. 'I know you're hard-up, Dad, so I'll take a reduction in pocket money this year – just give me £1 a week – on condition that you give double that next year and double again the next and so on, so that I get a bit more as I get older to take account of inflation.'

'Seems very fair,' said Dad, and Mum agreed.

Well, she was 18 when she left school and her parents had long since regretted the deal. Why?

Let's work it out:

Her weekly pocket money amount would increase each year like this:
£1, £2, £4, £8, £16, £32, £64, ...

By the age of 18 she would be receiving £64 pocket money per week.

The amounts could be expressed as powers of 2:
$1 = 2^0$, $2 = 2^1$, $4 = 2^2$, $8 = 2^3$, etc.

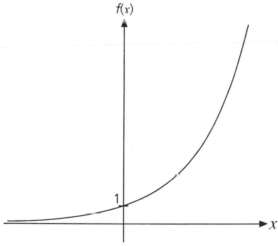

This is the graph of $f(x) - 2^x$
(Some negative values for x have also been taken.)
It shows exponential growth.
Exponential growth can be very rapid eventually.

The function $f(x) = a^x$ is an example of the exponential function. Its graph passes through the point (0, 1).

What will the graphs of $y = 3^x$ and $y = 0.5^x$ look like?
Plot points and draw them if you are not sure.

Graphical solutions

Here is the graph of
$y = x^3 - 3x$:

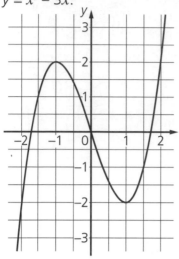

- **Example 1**
  Use the graph to find solutions for $x^3 - 3x = -x$.
  This is the same as solving $y = x^3 - 3x$
                  and $y = -x$ simultaneously.
  Draw in the line $y = -x$ on the graph and read off the
  intersections. You should get: $x = 0$, $x = 1.4$ and $x = -1.4$.

- **Example 2**
  For what values of k will $x^3 - 3x = k$ have three solutions?
  This is the same as solving $y = x^3 - 3x$
                  and $y = k$ simultaneously.
  Lines with equation $y = k$ are horizontal lines.
  If $k > 2$ or $k < -2$, then a horizontal line will cut the graph
  only once.
  If $-2 < k < 2$, then the horizontal line will cut the curve three
  times.

Iteration

- **Example**
  The equation $x^3 - 3x = 0$ has three solutions. (You can see this from the graph above as it
  crosses the x-axis at three points.) One solution is $x = 0$. Another lies between 1·5 and 2. Use
  an iterative method to find this root, correct to two decimal places.

  $f(x) = x^3 - 3x$ and $f(1.5) < 0$ and $f(2) > 0$

  You must narrow down the interval between 1·5 and 2 until you find more precisely where the
  curve cuts the x-axis. Each time you try the mid-point of the interval.

Put the results in a table:

root lies between	
1·5	2

Try $\dfrac{1.5 + 2}{2} = 1.75$

(1·75 is the mid-point of the interval from
1·5 to 2.)
$f(1.75) = 0.109 > 0$ enter:

1·5	1·75

Try $\dfrac{1.5 + 1.75}{2} = 1.625$

$f(1.625) = -0.584 < 0$ enter:

1·625	1·75
1·687	1·75
1·718	1·75
1·718	1·734
1·726	1·734

If you continue in this way, you will get the
values in the table opposite. (Check them
for yourself.)

You do not need to go any further, since both numbers are 1·73 correct to two decimal places.
The root is approximately 1·73, and by symmetry the third root is −1·73.

6. Maps, Plans and Similar Shapes

Similar shapes

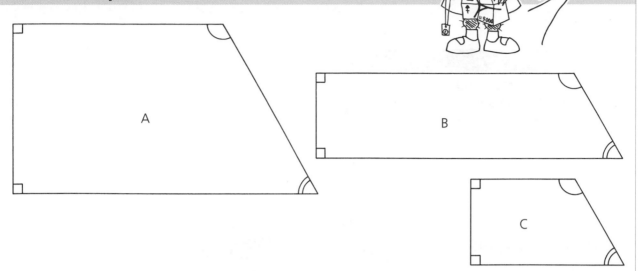

The above shapes are equiangular – they all have the same sizes of angles. The equal angles have been marked on the shapes.

You can see that A and C are **similar in shape**.
B, however, is not similar to A or C: it is too long compared to its height.

Measure the sides of A and C.

You will find that   A is an **enlargement** of C with scale factor 2,

and   C is a **reduction** of A with scale factor $\frac{1}{2}$.

> **TIP**
>
> Similar shapes are always equiangular.
> Equiangular shapes, however, do not have to be similar – unless they are triangles.

Maps – scale

A map is an example of a reduction – a reduction of the real world. A map must give the scale to which it is drawn.
For example, scale 1:50 000 means the real lengths are 50 000 times longer than on the map.
1 cm on the map stands for 50 000 cm = 500 m in the real world.

- **Example**
  The road (AB on the map) is 3·6 km long.

  What is the scale of this map?

       4 cm   represents   3·6 km
  so   1 cm   represents   0·9 km
                             = 900 m
                             = 90 000 cm
  So the scale of this map is 1:90 000.

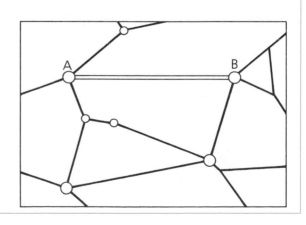

Maps – direction

This is a diagram showing compass points and three-figure bearings:

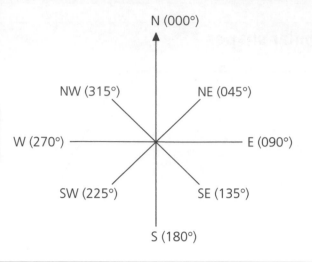

> **TIP**
>
> Use a protractor if you have to draw or measure a bearing in the exams.

Similar triangles

- **Example**
  From the point marked A, the tops of the two mountains are in line with each other:

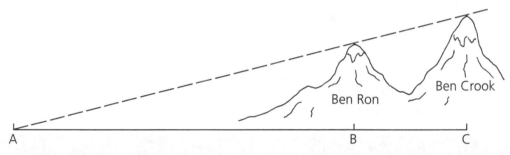

Ben Ron is 1931 feet high and Ben Crook 2557 feet high. The distance from A to B is 7·8 miles. How far is it from A to C?

> **TIP**
>
> Draw a simplified picture.

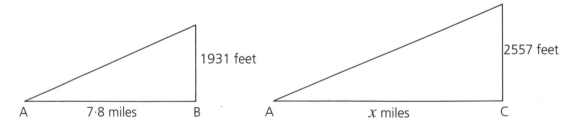

The scale factor for the enlargement is $\frac{2557}{1931}$

So $x = \frac{2557}{1931} \times 7\cdot8$ miles = 10·3 miles (to 1 decimal place).

Sketches and scale drawings

- A sketch is a **rough picture**, usually drawn to help you decide what calculations you need to make to solve a problem.
- A scale drawing must be **accurate**, with all angles and lines drawn to the **correct measurements**.

If an examination question says that answers obtained from scale drawings will receive no marks, then it is your knowledge of algebra and trigonometry which is being tested. Any diagrams you draw are only to help you understand the question.

If, however, a scale drawing is required, you must use the appropriate mathematical instruments as accurately as possible.

> **TIP**
>
> When drawing diagrams:
> - use a pencil, not a pen
> - write in lengths and angle sizes as you go along
> - if you are drawing North lines, make sure they are all parallel
> - if a scale is given (or suggested), use it
> - if you are choosing the scale yourself, make sure the diagram is clear and not too small
> - don't start too near the edge of the page.

Area of similar shapes

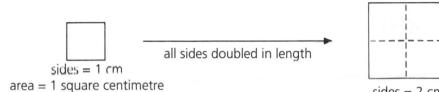

sides = 1 cm
area = 1 square centimetre

all sides doubled in length

sides = 2 cm
area = 4 square centimetres

The lengths are in the ratio 1:2.
The areas are in the ratio 1:4 (which is $1^2:2^2$).

- **Example**

A large photograph of area 108 cm² is to be reduced, using scale factor $\frac{1}{3}$, to give a smaller photograph. What will the area of the smaller photograph be?

Scale factor $\frac{1}{3}$ means lengths are in ratio 1:3

So areas are in ratio $1^2:3^2 = 1:9$

So the smaller photograph's area will be $\frac{1}{9}$ of 108 cm², which is 12 cm².

Bearings

- **Example**
The bearing of **B from A** is 075°. What is the bearing of **A from B**?

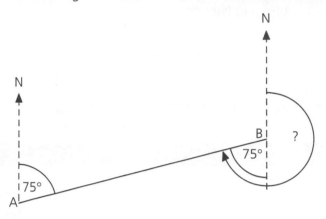

By drawing the North line at B, and marking a pair of alternate angles made by parallel lines, you can calculate the size of the angle marked with the arrow as 180° + 75°, which is 255°. The bearing of A from B is 255°.

> **TIP**
> Since all North lines are parallel, look for alternate and corresponding angles.
> Look back at page 14 if you have forgotten what these angles are.

More on similar triangles

- **Example**
These triangles are similar. Find the length of PQ. All lengths are measured in centimetres.

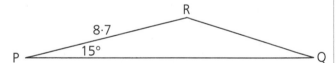

Before finding the scale factor, reposition the triangles so that the sides and angles correspond:

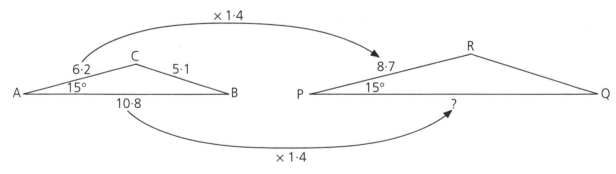

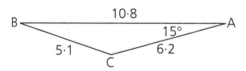

The scale factor for the enlargement is given by $\frac{8.7}{6.2}$, which is approximately 1·4.

The arrows on the diagram help to show this.

10·8 must be multiplied by the same scale factor to find PQ.

PQ = 10·8 × 1·4
     = 15·1 cm (to one decimal place)

© Leckie & Leckie

Volumes of similar shapes

- **Example 1**

  These two soup cans are similar in shape. The smaller tin holds 290 g of soup. How much does the larger tin hold?

  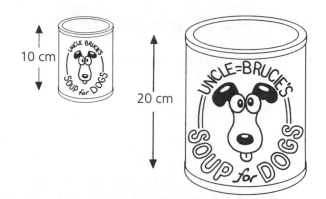

  You can see that their lengths are in the ratio 1:2 so their surface areas are in the ratio $1^2:2^2 = 1:4$ and their volumes are in the ratio $1^3:2^3 = 1:8$.

  So the larger tin holds 8 times as much. It holds 8×290 g = 2320 g or 2·32 kg.

  ESSENTIAL INFORMATION

  Similar shapes have
  - their lengths in the ratio $a:b$
  - their areas in the ratio $a^2:b^2$
  - their volumes in the ratio $a^3:b^3$

- **Example 2**

54 cm²

150 cm²

These two chocolate boxes are similar in shape. The larger box holds 1 kilogram of chocolates. The shaded triangles have areas as marked.

What weight of chocolates will the smaller box hold?

Let the sides be in ratio $a:b$.

From the picture, areas are in ratio $54:150 = 9:25$ (cancelling)
$$\text{So } a^2:b^2 = 9:25$$
$$\text{and so } a:b = 3:5$$

This means that the volumes are in the ratio $3^3:5^3 = 27:125$

Hence the weight of chocolates in the smaller box = $\frac{27}{125}$ of 1 kg = 216 g.

7. Proportion and Variation

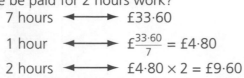

Direct and inverse proportion

(Generous Proportion)

- **Direct proportion example**
  Susan is paid £33·60 for 7 hours work.
  What will she be paid for 2 hours work?

  7 hours ◄──────► £33·60

  1 hour ◄──────► £$\frac{33·60}{7}$ = £4·80

  2 hours ◄──────► £4·80 × 2 = £9·60

  She will be paid £9·60 for two hours work.

- **Inverse proportion example**
  Last year it took 3 men 16 hours to weed a field, but this year 8 men have been employed to do the job. How long should it take this year?

  3 men ◄──────► 16 hours
  1 man ◄──────► 16 × 3 = 48 hours

  8 men ◄──────► 16 × $\frac{3}{8}$ = 6 hours

  The job should take 6 hours this year.

- How do you know which is direct and which is inverse proportion?
  Notice this:

Pie charts

- **Example**

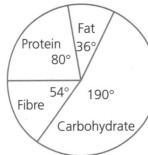

The pie chart shows the nutritional content of 'Cracklie' cereal bars. If each bar weighs 40 g, how many grams of fibre does a bar contain?

In the pie chart, fibre is represented by 54° (out of a total of 360°).

Weight of fibre $= \frac{54}{360}$ of 40 g

$= 6$ g.

Ratio

- **Example 1**

Butter Icing Recipe

Beat together
100 g icing sugar
50 g butter

The recipe shows that to make 150 g of butter icing you need 100 g of icing sugar and 50 g of butter.

- What should be used to make 1·5 kg of butter icing?
  Ratio of sugar:butter is 100:50 or, more simply, 2:1.

  Since 1·5 kg = 1500 g, split 1500 g in the ratio 2:1 (total of 3 parts).
  Divide 1500 by 3, giving 500 g in each part.
  Of sugar (2 parts) you need 1000 grams. Of butter (1 part) you need 500 grams.

- For chocolate icing, 25 g of cocoa should be added to the basic mixture. What is the ratio of sugar:butter:cocoa?

sugar	:	butter	:	cocoa
100 g	:	50 g	:	25 g

  The ratio is: 4   :   2   :   1   (total of 7 parts)

  So $\frac{4}{7}$ of the required weight of chocolate icing should be sugar, $\frac{2}{7}$ butter and $\frac{1}{7}$ cocoa.

- **Example 2**

Mark paid 7 francs for 1 litre of milk while on holiday in France. Back in Scotland he paid 39p for 1 pint. Given that 1 pint is 0·568 litres and £1 was worth 10·5 francs at the time of his holiday, in which country was milk cheaper, France or Scotland?
One way to compare is to find the cost of a litre in Sterling (British money) in each country:

- In France: 10·5 francs = £1 = 100p

  $1 \text{ franc} = \frac{100}{10\cdot5} \text{ pence}$

  $7 \text{ francs} = \frac{100}{10\cdot5} \times 7$

  $= 66\cdot66\ldots$

  $= £0\cdot6667$

- In Scotland: 1 pint = 0·568 litre, costing 39p

  $1 \text{ litre cost } 39p \times \frac{1}{0\cdot568}$

  $= 68\cdot66p$

  So 1 litre cost 69p in Scotland.

So 1 litre cost approximately 67p in France.

So the milk was cheaper in France.

Direct variation

- **Example 1**
  Susan's pay (given on page 34) is shown on this graph:
  This is a direct variation graph.
  It is a straight line through the origin.
  Pay varies directly as number of hours.
  (Pay ∝ number of hours.)

Direct variation (cont.)

- **Example 2**
  A table of car braking distances is given below. It is known that the braking distance D varies directly as the square of the speed S. Draw a graph to show this and find a formula linking D and S.

Speed S *(mph)*	20	30	40	50	60	70
Braking distance D *(feet)*	20	45	80	125	180	245

First, draw the graph of D plotted against S. Since this graph is not a straight line, D does not vary directly as S.
Next, calculate values of S^2 and make a new line in the table:

S^2	400	900	1600	2500	3600	4900
D	20	45	80	125	180	245

Now, if you draw the graph of S^2 plotted against D, you will get a straight line through the origin.
Since D varies directly as S^2 ($D \propto S^2$), so $D = kS^2$ for some constant k.
From the table you can see that D is always $S^2 \div 20$. (Check this.)

The formula linking D and S is: $D = \dfrac{S^2}{20}$

Inverse variation

- **Example 1**
  This graph shows the time taken to weed a field plotted against the number of men (on page 34).

  This is an inverse variation graph.

  T varies inversely as N. $T \propto \dfrac{1}{N}$

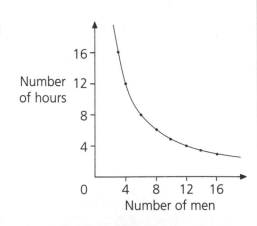

- **Example 2**
  The time, T minutes, taken to cook pork in a microwave oven is inversely proportional to the power setting, P watts. It takes 4 minutes to cook a piece of pork on setting 600 watts. How long will it take to cook the pork on setting 800 watts?

  $T \propto \dfrac{1}{P}$ so $T = \dfrac{k}{P}$ Substitute values and find k: $4 = \dfrac{k}{600} \Rightarrow k = 2400$.

  The formula is $T = \dfrac{2400}{P}$ so if P = 800 watts, $T = \dfrac{2400}{800} = 3$ minutes.

  It will take 3 minutes to cook the pork on 800 watts.

Graph of $f(x) = \frac{a}{x}$

Compare the equation $T = \dfrac{k}{P}$ (in the previous example) with $f(x) = \dfrac{a}{x}$.

k and a are both constants. You can see the similarity in the equations. The graphs too will be similar:

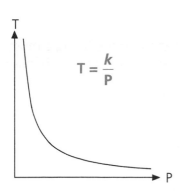

$$T = \frac{k}{P}$$

$$f(x) = \frac{a}{x}$$

Try choosing a value for a, e.g. $a = 12$, and plot points on the curve $y = \dfrac{a}{x}$, remembering to take some negative values for x as well as positive values. Its shape will be similar to the graph $f(x) = \dfrac{a}{x}$ above. Try a negative value of a as well.

Joint variation

- **Example**
  The time taken for a box to slide down a delivery chute varies directly as the length of the chute and inversely as the square root of the difference in height of the top and bottom.
  When the chute is 16 m long and the top is 4 m higher than the bottom, the box takes 10 seconds to slide down the chute.
  To reduce the risk of damage it is decided to lengthen the chute by 4 m but to keep the height difference the same.
  How long will it now take for the box to slide down the chute?
  Symbols: L for length, T for time, H for height difference.
  Pick out the important information:

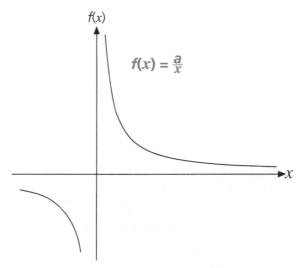

  Time: varies directly as L and varies inversely as $\sqrt{H}$

  So $T \propto \dfrac{L}{\sqrt{H}}$ or $T = \dfrac{kL}{\sqrt{H}}$

  Substitute in values: $10 = \dfrac{k \times 16}{\sqrt{4}} \Rightarrow 16k = 20 \Rightarrow k = \dfrac{5}{4}$

  Formula: $T = \dfrac{5L}{4\sqrt{H}}$ so now $T = \dfrac{5 \times 20}{4\sqrt{4}} = 12{\cdot}5$

  It now takes 12·5 seconds for the box to slide down the chute.

8. Triangles and Trigonometry

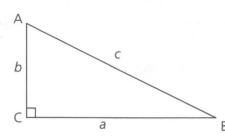

The Theorem of Pythagoras

The Theorem of Pythagoras is true for all right-angled triangles:

A

b

c

C

a

B

$AB^2 = AC^2 + BC^2$
(See page 46 for an example.)
Similarly, if you find that $a^2 = b^2 + c^2$, then the triangle must be right-angled. This is the converse of Pythagoras' Theorem.

One use of Pythagoras' Theorem is to find the lengths of sloping lines on a grid.

- **Example**
  Find the length of AB.
  By counting, you see that
  AC = 7 units and BC = 4 units.

  $AB^2 = AC^2 + BC^2$
  $= 49 + 16 = 65$

  so AB = $\sqrt{65}$ = 8·1 units
  (to 1 decimal place).

B (5, 3)

A
(−2, −1)

C

Trigonometry in right-angled triangles

ESSENTIAL INFORMATION

You must know which sides to use to find sine, cosine or tangent of an angle:

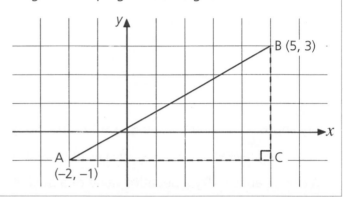

$$\sin x° = \frac{O}{H} \qquad \cos x° = \frac{A}{H} \qquad \tan x° = \frac{O}{A}$$

Remember: '**Soh Cah Toa**'!

To find a trigonometric ratio, use the [sin], [cos] and [tan] keys on your calculator.

For example, cos 64° = 0·438 (Check this for yourself.)

To find an angle, use the [inv] key, then [sin], [cos] or [tan].

For example, if sin $x°$ = 0·312, then $x°$ = 18·2° (to 1 decimal place).

[inv] might be [2nd F] on your calculator. Check that you know how to use your own calculator for trigonometric calculations.

Gradient, angles of elevation and depression

- **Example 1**

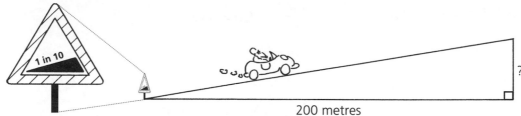

The sign shows that this road climbs 1 metre vertically for every 10 metres horizontally. If this hill is 200 metres horizontally, then the car will have climbed one-tenth of that in height by the time it reaches the top, that is, 20 metres.

- **Example 2**

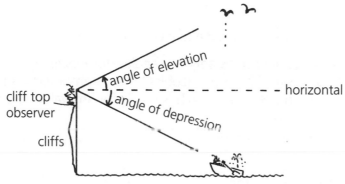

If the boat is 230 metres from the cliff top observer, and the angle of depression is 40°, how far from the cliffs is the boat?

Draw a simplified diagram:
d stands for the distance you have to find.

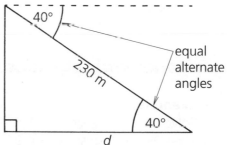

$$\cos 40° = \frac{d}{230}$$

so $d = 230 \cos 40° = 176{\cdot}19\ldots$

The boat is 176 metres (to the nearest metre) from the cliffs.

Trigonometric functions and their graphs

ESSENTIAL INFORMATION

Learn the graphs of $f(x) = \cos x°$ and $f(x) = \sin x°$, as shown below and on page 40:

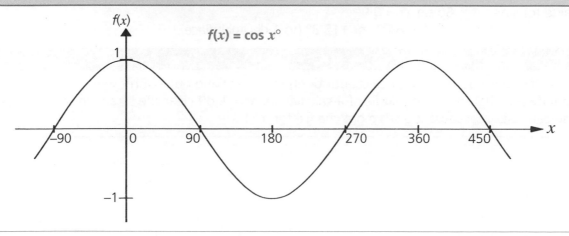

Trigonometric functions and their graphs (cont.)

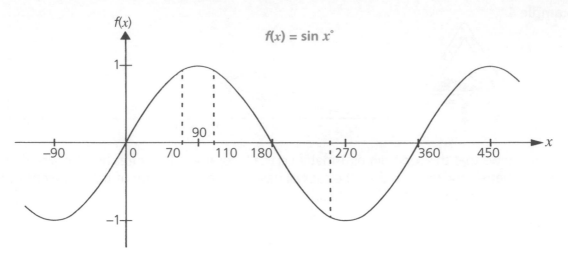

The period of both of the functions $f(x) = \sin x°$ and $f(x) = \cos x°$ is 360°.

From the symmetry, you can see relationships between angles, for example,

	$\sin 70° = \sin 110°$	(Look at the graph of $f(x) = \sin x°$ to see this.)
or, in general,	$\sin a° = \sin (180 - a)°$	(This is true for any value of a.)
Also	$\sin 70° = -\sin 250°$	
which, in general, is	$\sin a° = -\sin (180 + a)°$	

There are other similar relationships for cosine and tangent. These can be seen from their graphs. You can also remember them from the diagram opposite:

sin +ve $(180 - x)°$	all +ve $x°$
$(180 + x)°$ tan +ve	$(360 - x)°$ cos +ve

Trigonometric equations

- **Example**

  Solve $2 \sin x° = 1·8$ $0 \leqslant x < 360$

  so $\sin x° = 0·9$

  and $x = 64·15\ldots$

> **TIP**
>
> Just a minute! Most trig. equations have more than one answer.
> You will lose marks if you don't check that you have found **all** possible solutions!

From the graph of $\sin x°$, you know that $64·15\ldots°$ and $(180 - 64·15\ldots)°$ will have the same value for sine.   So $\sin x° = 0·9$

$\Rightarrow x° = 64·2°$ or $115·8°$ (to 1 decimal place).

> **TIP**
>
> Leave all your figures on your calculator during your working out. Don't write down rounded-off figures in the middle of a calculation, and don't clear the screen in the middle of the calculation because it gives more chance for mistakes.

Sine and cosine rules and the area of triangle formula

Look back at page 38 for how to name the sides of a triangle.

Sine rule	Area of a triangle formula	Cosine rule
$\dfrac{a}{\sin A} = \dfrac{b}{\sin B} = \dfrac{c}{\sin C}$	area $= \frac{1}{2}ab \sin C$	$a^2 = b^2 + c^2 - 2bc \cos A$ or $\cos A = \dfrac{b^2 + c^2 - a^2}{2bc}$

- **Example 1**

Two coastguard stations receive a distress signal from a ship at sea. From the first station B, the ship is on a bearing of 248°. From station C, which is 30 km south of B, the ship is on a bearing of 310°. How far is the ship from the nearer of the two coastguard stations?

From the given information, the sketch opposite can be drawn.

Calculate the third angle: 180° − (68° + 50°) = 62°

Since the longest side is opposite the largest angle, the first station is nearer.

Using the sine rule, $\dfrac{30}{\sin 62°} = \dfrac{AB}{\sin 50°}$

$\Rightarrow AB = \dfrac{30 \sin 50°}{\sin 62°} = 26\cdot02$

It is 26·0 km (to 3 significant figures) to the nearer coastguard station.

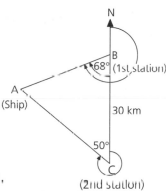

- **Example 2**

The area of triangle PQR is 20 cm². PQ = 8 cm and QR = 6 cm. Investigate the size of angle Q.

The area formula can be written: area $= \frac{1}{2}rp \sin Q$

so $20 = \frac{1}{2} \times 8 \times 6 \times \sin Q$

$$\sin Q = \dfrac{20}{\frac{1}{2} \times 8 \times 6} = 0\cdot833\ldots$$

hence angle Q = 56° or 124° (to the nearest degree).

If you find the two answers puzzling, the sketch below shows why the base and height of the two triangles below are equal in length, and so have the same area.

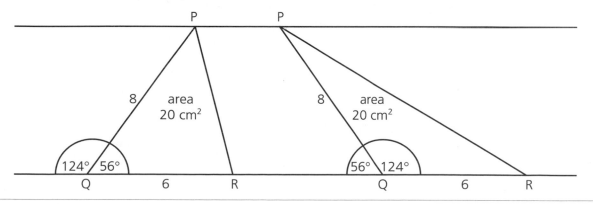

Trigonometric identities

ESSENTIAL INFORMATION

$\tan x° = \dfrac{\sin x°}{\cos x°}$ and $\sin^2 x° + \cos^2 x° = 1$ These are true for all values of x.

Remember also that $\sin^2 x°$ is the way to write $(\sin x°)^2$.

Trigonometry in three dimensions

- **Example**
  Find the size of the angle between the space diagonal AG and the base of the cuboid opposite. (All lengths are in metres).

  First identify the correct angle, before you use trigonometry.

  The projection of AG on the base is the line EG.

  So the required angle is $A\hat{G}E$.

  Using the Theorem of Pythagoras in triangle HGE, check that EG = 10 m.

  Triangle AGE is right-angled at E (since AE is vertical and EG is horizontal).

  So in triangle AGE, $\tan \hat{G} = \dfrac{5}{10} = 0.5$

  which gives $\hat{G} = 27°$ to the nearest degree.

  The angle between the space diagonal and the base is 27°.

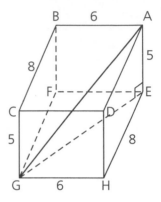

Families of trigonometric curves

In these sketches, different values of constant k have been chosen and the graphs drawn.

- **Family** $f(x) = \sin x° + k$

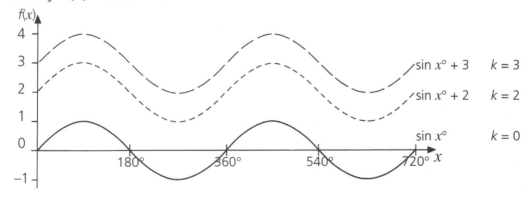

Adding k to $\sin x°$ moves the graph up or down by k units.

- Family $f(x) = \sin kx°$

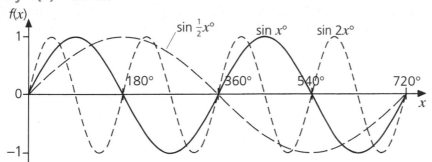

The period is altered: $\sin kx°$ will have k complete cycles in 360°.

- Family $f(x) = k \sin x°$

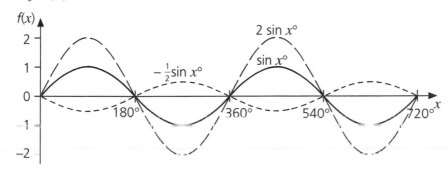

The amplitude is altered: it is k times as large.

- Family $f(x) = \sin(x + k)°$

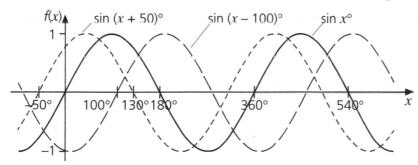

Adding a constant to x moves the graph along the x-axis.
For example, $\sin(x + 50)°$ is the graph of $\sin x°$ moved 50° to the left.

If the graph of $\sin x°$ is moved 90° to the left, it will be the same as the graph of $\cos x°$, that is, $\sin(x + 90)° = \cos x°$.

You could draw some families of cosine curves, putting $\cos x°$ in place of $\sin x°$ in the families above and on page 42, choosing some values of k, and plotting the graphs.

Families of trigonometric curves (cont.)

- **Example**

  The graph below shows how the water level in a harbour rises and falls with the tide. The depth of water in the harbour has been plotted against the number of hours since midnight.

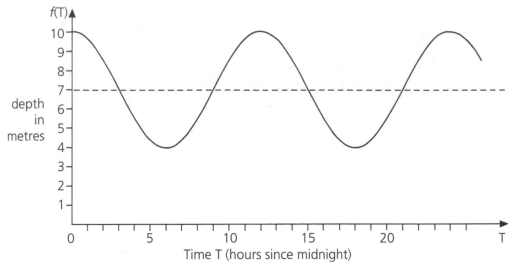

The equation of the graph can be written in the form:
$$f(T) = 3 \cos (30T)° + A$$

- Find the value of A.

> **TIP**
>
> A is the constant which moves the graph up or down – look at the family at the bottom of page 42. This graph has been moved up by 7 (look at the dashed line) so A = 7.

So $f(T) = 3 \cos (30T)° + 7$

- A yacht is berthed in the harbour. It cannot leave until the water level rises above 8 metres. At what time after 0500 will it be able to leave the harbour?

The depth is 8 metres when $\qquad 3 \cos (30T)° + 7 = 8$

which means
$$3 \cos (30T)° = 1$$
$$\cos (30T)° = 0.333\ldots$$
$$30T = 70.52\ldots° \text{ or } 289.47\ldots°$$
$$T = 2.35\ldots \text{ or } 9.65\ldots$$

Since 2·35 hours after midnight is before 0500, this cannot be the correct answer.

So the yacht can leave 9·65… hours after midnight, which is 0939 hours.

If you add multiples of 360° to the values for 30T°, you can also get high and low tides for the following days.

9. The Circle

Circumference and area

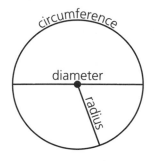

ESSENTIAL INFORMATION

Circumference of a circle = π × diameter
(C = πd or C = 2πr)

Area of a circle = π × square of radius
(A = πr²)

π is approximately 3·14 but get used to using the π button on your calculator all the time.

- **Example**

A cake, 20 cm in diameter, is to be iced on the top and have a decorative frill put around it. Find the area to be iced, and the length of the frill.

Its radius is half its diameter, so *r* = 10 cm.

The area to be iced is a circle.
So area = πr² = π × 10 × 10
= 314 cm² (to 3 significant figures).

The frill goes around the circumference.
C = π × d = π × 20
= 62·8 cm (to 3 significant figures).

TIP

Always **be sensible about rounding** if you get an answer with many figures after the decimal point. This often happens when using π.

For example, if your calculator gives the final answer 37·259641, don't write all that down. That wouldn't be sensible! 37·3 would be a good answer to write down!

A good idea with measurements is to make them the same accuracy as the measurements given to you in the question. If you can't decide, use 3 significant figures.

Angle in a semicircle

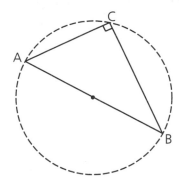

ESSENTIAL INFORMATION

If AB is a diameter and C is a point on the circumference, then angle $A\hat{C}B = 90°$.

Angle in a semicircle (cont.)

> **TIP**
>
> When there is an angle in a semicircle, you can use Pythagoras' Theorem or Trig.

- **Example**

  The last diagram on page 45 represents a circle whose radius is 5 m and which has AC = 6 m. Find the length of BC and the size of angle B.

  Using the Theorem of Pythagoras: $AC^2 + BC^2 = AB^2$

  $$6^2 + BC^2 = 10^2$$
  $$\text{so} \quad BC^2 = 100 - 36 = 64$$
  $$\text{and} \quad BC = 8 \text{ m}$$

  Using trigonometry:

  $$\tan A\hat{B}C = \frac{AC}{BC} = \frac{6}{8} = 0.75$$

  $$\text{so} \quad A\hat{B}C = 36.9° \text{ (to 3 significant figures).}$$

Tangents

In the diagram below, TS is a tangent and OA is a radius which meets the tangent at A. This means $O\hat{A}T$ and $O\hat{A}S$ are both 90°.

UC and UB are both tangents to the circle below, so they are equal in length. OCUB is a kite.

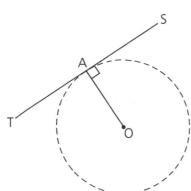

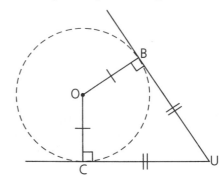

Arcs and sectors

Drawing radii in a circle divides the circumference into arcs and the area into sectors.

The ratios into which they are divided will be the same.

Here are some examples of equal ratios in the diagram opposite:

$$\frac{\text{size of } A\hat{O}B}{\text{size of } B\hat{O}C} = \frac{\text{length of arc AB}}{\text{length of arc BC}} = \frac{\text{area of sector AOB}}{\text{area of sector BOC}}$$

and $$\frac{\text{size of } A\hat{O}B}{\text{size of } A\hat{O}C} = \frac{\text{length of arc AB}}{\text{length of arc AC}} = \frac{\text{area of sector AOB}}{\text{area of sector AOC}}$$

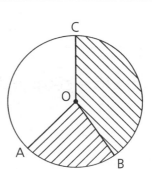

Arcs and sectors (cont.)

- **Example**
  In the last diagram on the previous page, angle $\hat{AOB}$ is 70° and arc AB is 4·3 units.

  Find
  (a) the circumference of the circle
  (b) the radius of the circle and
  (c) the area of the sector AOB.

  > **TIP**
  >
  > The **sector** AOB is not the same as **triangle** AOB.

Write down suitable ratios:

(a) $\dfrac{\text{circumference}}{4\cdot3 \text{ units}} = \dfrac{360°}{70°}$

$C = \dfrac{360}{70} \times 4\cdot3 = 22\cdot1$ units (to 1 dp).

(b) $C = 2\pi r$, so $r = \dfrac{C}{2\pi} = \dfrac{22\cdot1\ldots}{2 \times \pi} = 3\cdot519\ldots$

radius = 3·52 units (to 3 sf).

(c) $\dfrac{\text{area of sector AOB}}{\text{area of circle}} = \dfrac{70}{360}$

area of sector AOB $= \dfrac{70}{360} \times \pi r^2$

$= 7\cdot57$ units^2 (to 3 significant figures).

Chords

In each of these diagrams, OS is a radius and PQ is a chord of the circle:

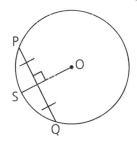

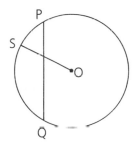

PQ is perpendicular to OS and OS bisects PQ.

PQ is **not** perpendicular to OS and OS does **not** bisect PQ.

- **Example**
  The diameter of this oil tanker is 4 metres and the width of the oil surface is 3·2 metres. What reading will the dipstick give for the depth of oil in the tank? (The tanker is less than half full.)

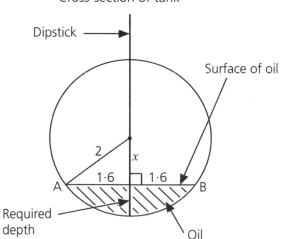

Since the oil surface AB is horizontal and the dipstick is vertical, they meet at right angles. The diameter (dipstick) bisects the chord AB.

In the triangle, $x^2 = 2^2 - 1\cdot6^2$ which gives $x = 1\cdot2$. (Check it.)

The depth of oil is $(2 - 1\cdot2)$ metres, so the dipstick reading is 0·8 metres.

10. Statistics

Mean, mode and range

Kerry wasn't looking forward to telling her parents what she'd got in her Trigonometry test – seven out of twenty. All her friends agreed it had been a really awful test. Kerry's dad said, 'Well, seven out of twenty doesn't sound very good, but what were the other marks like? Was it really just a very hard test? What was the class average?'

Here are the marks:

$$\begin{array}{cccccccccc}
2 & 8 & 11 & 19 & 7 & 6 & 5 & 2 & 10 & 3 \\
5 & 5 & 3 & 7 & 5 & 13 & 12 & 8 & 5 & 4
\end{array}$$

$\text{Mean} = \dfrac{\text{total of all marks}}{\text{number of pupils}} = \dfrac{140}{20} = 7$ ('Mean' is what most people mean by 'average'.)

Kerry's dad said, 'Right, so you don't need to worry too much. You got an exactly fair share of all the marks going.'

Here is a **frequency table** for the marks.

Mark	Frequency	Mark × Frequency
2	2	4
3	2	6
4	1	4
5	5	25
6	1	6
7	2	14
8	2	16
9	0	0
10	1	10
11	1	11
12	1	12
13	1	13
14	0	0
15	0	0
16	0	0
17	0	0
18	0	0
19	1	19
	total 20	total 140

The mean can be calculated from a frequency table by dividing the total of the 'mark × frequency' column by the total of the 'frequency' column.

Jackie had his story ready for his mum. 'I only got five out of twenty, but it's alright because lots of us got five. More people got 5 than any other mark.'

Mean, mode and range (cont.)

The mode is the most commonly occurring mark. Look down the frequency column and find what mark has the highest frequency. You should find that for the test marks the mode is 5.

Jackie is right – more people got 5 than any other mark. But does this mean his test mark was alright? His mum wasn't totally impressed. 'That might mean far too many of you didn't revise! Tell me this – what were the best and worst marks?'

Highest mark   19
Lowest mark   2

The range (the difference between highest and lowest marks) is 17.

Jackie's mark seems pretty bad considering all that. Jackie's mum said, 'So some people got good marks then! I think you should get up to your room and get some homework done!'

Median

Their teacher, Miss Cameron, wasn't too happy either. Had she not spent enough time on the Trig? Had they been spending too much time on their English folios instead of their Maths homework? She decided to give them some more revision, then retest the bottom half of the class.

The median divides the marks into the upper and lower halves.

Marks in order:

2 2 3 3 4 5 5 5 5 5 6 7 7 8 8 10 11 12 13 19

There is not one particular mark in the middle because there are 20 marks, so you must go between the tenth and the eleventh marks.

$$\text{median} = \frac{5 + 6}{2} = 5{\cdot}5$$

Everyone with less than 5·5 will have to resit.

Probability

The deputy head is on a campaign to improve exam results and thinks dropping into classrooms, picking a pupil at random and finding out about his or her latest test mark will give him an idea of how the campaign is progressing. (The Maths department think it's time the deputy head did a course in Statistics.) Anyway, Miss Cameron is worried: 'If he comes in here today, chances are he'll pick someone who has less than half marks. It won't look good!'

Count up how many pupils had marks less than 10.

Probability of a pupil picked at random having a mark of less than 10:

$$\text{Probability} = \frac{\text{number of pupils with mark less than 10}}{\text{total number of pupils}} = \frac{15}{20} = \frac{3}{4} \text{ or } 0{\cdot}75$$

Stem and leaf chart

The class's next Maths topic is Statistics so Miss Cameron decides that the class should use their test marks as data for some graphs.

Here is the raw data for their recent Algebra test, out of 40:

13 34 32 24 28 29 19 16 31 14 26 9 22 29 38 26 40 36 23 18

The data can be shown in a stem and leaf diagram or stem plot. The tens of the marks make the stem, and the units make the leaves:

```
          Algebra Test Scores
              0 | 9
              1 | 3 4 6 8 9
              2 | 2 3 4 6 6 8 9 9
              3 | 1 2 4 6 8
              4 | 0
```

n = 20   3 | 4   represents a mark of 34

Notice you must put the digits in the leaves in order of size, and you must state at the bottom how many pieces of data there are (20 in this case because that's how many people sat the test).

A back-to-back stem and leaf chart would have another set of test marks, with the same stem but the digits coming out to the left instead of to the right. It is then easy to compare the two sets of data.

For example, if the first three marks in the Trig test were entered as three pieces of data for the other side of a back-to back stem and leaf chart, it would look like this:

```
        8 2  | 0 | 9
          1  | 1 | 3 4 6 8 9
             | 2 | 2 3 4 6 6 8 9 9
             | 3 | 1 2 4 6 8
             | 4 | 0
```

Practise entering the rest of the data yourself.

However, it would not be sensible to compare the two tests using this statistical method since one test is out of 20 and the other is out of 40.

Scattergraph

The next task the class does is constructing a scattergraph using the ordered pairs (mark in Trig test, mark in Algebra test) as points. For example, as Jackie scored 5 in Trig but 38 in Algebra, the point representing his marks will be (5, 38). You can see all 20 points plotted on the scattergraph on page 51.

The graph shows positive correlation: in general, a good mark in one test goes with a good mark in the other.

Scattergraph (cont.)

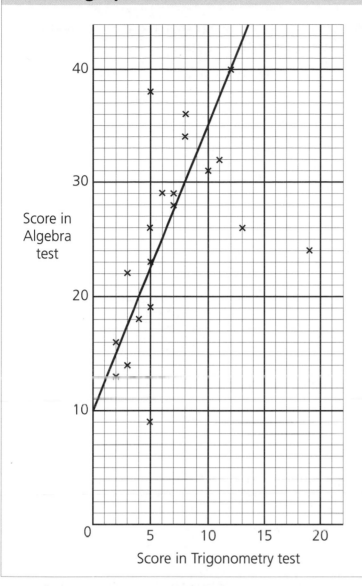

Score in Algebra test

Score in Trigonometry test

A best-fitting line has been drawn in the direction where the points lie. Approximately half of the points lie on each side of the line. The point (7, 28) represents someone in the class who performed about the same, relative to the rest of the class, in both tests, as the point is very close to the line.

Jackie's point is far from the line and shows that he did very much better in Algebra than in Trig. He's going straight home to remind his Mum about that good Algebra test score.

Find the point for Matthew (19, 24) who was away on a family holiday while the class were learning Algebra. It looks like he's got some catching up on missed work to do to make up for that fortnight of fun.

Shona (12, 40), at the top right position, looks like the star pupil and Debbie (2, 13) ought to be considering fitting in some extra revision.

Equation of line of best fit

Just as with any line on the co-ordinate plane, you can find the equation by considering the gradient and intercept on the vertical axis.

Look at the scattergraph again. The line of best fit cuts the vertical axis (y-axis) at (0, 10) and rises 5 units vertically for every 2 horizontally, giving a gradient of $\frac{5}{2}$.

The equation is $y = \frac{5}{2}x + 10$, which simplifies to $2y = 5x + 20$

Upper and lower quartiles, and semi-interquartile range

Miss Cameron decides that this month's 'praise and progress' points should go to the people who did well in the Trig test. She will pick the top quarter of the class.

The upper quartile and lower quartile cut off the top and bottom quarters – in this case the top five and the bottom five pupils.

Marks in order:

    2 2 3 3 4   5 5 5 5 5   6 7 7 8 8   10 11 12 13 19

The 20 marks are grouped in 4 equal groups of 5.

lower quartile = 4·5 (halfway between 4 and 5)
upper quartile = 9 (average of 8 and 10)

'Praise and progress' points will go to those with marks over 9.

Semi-interquartile range = $\frac{1}{2}$(upper quartile – lower quartile) = $\frac{9-4\cdot5}{2}$ = $\frac{4\cdot5}{2}$ = 2·25.

Box and dot plots

Miss Cameron shows the class how to draw a dot plot and a box plot of the Trig test scores.

- **Dot plot**

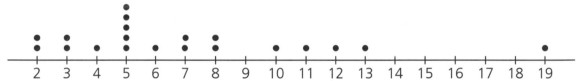

The dot plot shows how spread out the top marks were and how many people got low marks.

- **Box plot**

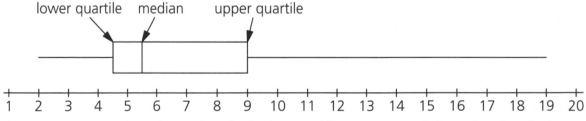

The 'whiskers' on a box plot end at the highest and lowest pieces of data, showing the range.

Cumulative frequency

Cumulative frequency counts the number of marks less than or equal to a given mark. For example, a frequency table can have an extra column where all the marks up to the current mark (meaning that mark and all the marks less than it) are counted up.

Here is a frequency table with data from page 48 and the cumulative frequency column added:

Mark	Frequency	Cumulative frequency
2	2	2
3	2	4
4	1	5
5	5	10
6	1	11
7	2	13
8	2	15
9	0	15
10	1	16
11	1	17
12	1	18
13	1	19
14	0	19
15	0	19
16	0	19
17	0	19
18	0	19
19	1	20

How many people scored 7 or less?

The answer 13 can be read in the cumulative frequency column next to the mark 7. It is also easy to calculate the median or quartiles – do this now from the frequency table and check your answers against those in the appropriate sections of this chapter.

Constructing pie charts

- **Example**
  40 people were asked about their holiday destinations. The results were:

Scotland	14
Rest of Britain	8
Other parts of Europe	15
Rest of the World	3
	40

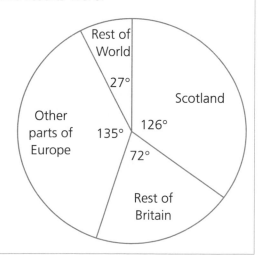

Draw a pie chart for these people's holiday destinations:
40 pieces of data need to fit 360°. That's 9° each.

Scotland has 14 × 9° = 126°
Check the rest of these angle sizes – work them out for yourself!

Standard deviation

The range and quartiles give an idea of how much the data is spread out from the mean. Standard deviation is a more precise way to measure the spread of the data.

In the Credit exam, you are required to use a standard deviation formula to calculate the standard deviation of a data set. There are two acceptable formulae which you can use and both are given in the formula list in the exam paper. You should use whichever one your teacher recommends or the one you feel most comfortable with. In the end it's up to you.

ESSENTIAL INFORMATION

The formulae are: $s = \sqrt{\dfrac{\Sigma(x - \bar{x})^2}{n-1}}$ and $s = \sqrt{\dfrac{\Sigma x^2 - \frac{1}{n}(\Sigma x)^2}{n-1}}$

The symbols in the above formulae mean:

n the number of pieces of data
x a piece of data
$\bar{x}$ 'x bar': the mean of the data
Σ the sum of
s standard deviation

So $\bar{x}$ (the mean) is found by dividing Σx (the sum of all the data) by n (the number of pieces of data):

$$\bar{x} = \frac{\Sigma x}{n}$$

TIP

Be careful of the difference between $(\Sigma x)^2$ and Σx^2.

The example on the next page is worked out both ways. Remember that you do not need to do it both ways (or even know how to do it both ways). You may even be able to do the whole thing on your calculator but make sure that you also understand at least one written method. Also, make sure it is clear to the examiner which method you are using.

You will now find the mean and standard deviation of a sample.

Here are the numbers of half-day absences of a sample of S4 pupils:

0 0 2 5 6 7 8 12 15 28

Mean $= \dfrac{\Sigma x}{n} = \dfrac{83}{10} = 8 \cdot 3$

So, on average, S4 pupils are absent 8·3 half-days each. But, as we all know, some pupils are never off and a small minority are absent a great deal. The standard deviation will give an idea of how much the amounts of absence vary from 8·3.

Standard deviation (cont.)

Using the first formula:

x	$x - \bar{x}$	$(x - \bar{x})^2$
0	−8·3	68·89
0	−8·3	68·89
2	−6·3	39·69
5	−3·3	10·89
6	−2·3	5·29
7	−1·3	1·69
8	−0·3	0·09
12	3·7	13·69
15	6·7	44·89
28	19·7	388·09
$\sum x = 83$		$\sum(x - \bar{x})^2 = 642 \cdot 10$

$$s = \sqrt{\frac{\sum(x - \bar{x})^2}{n - 1}} = \sqrt{\frac{642 \cdot 1}{9}} = \sqrt{71 \cdot 34\ldots} = 8 \cdot 45 \text{ (to 2 decimal places)}$$

Using the second formula:

x	x^2
0	0
0	0
2	4
5	25
6	36
7	49
8	64
12	144
15	225
28	784
$\sum x = 83$	$\sum x^2 = 1331$

$$s = \sqrt{\frac{\sum x^2 - \frac{1}{n}(\sum x)^2}{n - 1}} = \sqrt{\frac{1331 - \frac{83^2}{10}}{9}} = \sqrt{\frac{642 \cdot 1}{9}} = \sqrt{71 \cdot 34\ldots} = 8 \cdot 45 \text{ (to 2 decimal places)}$$

11. Formulae given in the Exam Papers

General level formulae

These formulae are given in the General level exam paper:

- Circumference of a circle: $C = \pi d$
- Area of a circle: $A = \pi r^2$
- Curved surface area of a cylinder: $A = 2\pi rh$
- Volume of a cylinder: $V = \pi r^2 h$
- Volume of a triangular prism: $V = Ah$
- Theorem of Pythagoras: $c^2 = a^2 + b^2$

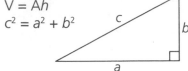

- Trigonometric ratios in a right-angled triangle:

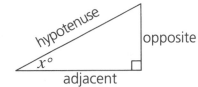

$$\sin x° = \frac{\text{opposite}}{\text{hypotenuse}}$$

$$\cos x° = \frac{\text{adjacent}}{\text{hypotenuse}}$$

$$\tan x° = \frac{\text{opposite}}{\text{adjacent}}$$

- Gradient:

$$\text{Gradient} = \frac{\text{vertical height}}{\text{horizontal distance}}$$

ESSENTIAL INFORMATION

If you are sitting the Credit level exam paper, you must **learn** these General level formulae as they are not given in the Credit level exam paper.

Credit level formulae

These formulae are given in the Credit level exam paper:

- The roots of $ax^2 + bx + c$ are: $x = \dfrac{-b \pm \sqrt{b^2 - 4ac}}{2a}$

- Sine rule: $\dfrac{a}{\sin A} = \dfrac{b}{\sin B} = \dfrac{c}{\sin C}$

- Cosine rule: $a^2 = b^2 + c^2 - 2bc \cos A$ or $\cos A = \dfrac{b^2 + c^2 - a^2}{2bc}$

- Area of a triangle: $\text{area} = \frac{1}{2} ab \sin C$

- Volume of a sphere: $V = \frac{4}{3}\pi r^3$
- Volume of a cone: $V = \frac{1}{3}\pi r^2 h$
- Volume of a cylinder: $V = \pi r^2 h$

- Sample standard deviation: $s = \sqrt{\dfrac{\Sigma(x - \bar{x})^2}{n - 1}} = \sqrt{\dfrac{\Sigma x^2 - \frac{1}{n}(\Sigma x)^2}{n - 1}}$ where n is the sample size.